Universal Edition

GW00771214

for Carey Blyton

MIKE CORNICK'S
BOOGIE PIANO
D U E T S

www.**universaledition**.com

vienna · london · new york

UE 18 796

ISMN 979-0-008-06131-8
UPC 8-03452-04680-6
ISBN 978-3-7024-2888-4

CONTENTS

BOOGIE-WOOGIE

IT IS VERY DIFFICULT TO DETERMINE the exact origins of the piano style which we now recognise as *boogie-woogie* or even to establish how it earned its unlikely name. Amongst the variety of explanations on offer, the often quoted claim that the word was invented by Charlie 'Cow Cow' Davenport (born in 1895 in Alabama) now seems improbable. He linked the term to the bogey man and the generally low-life associations of the music, but at least one source traces the origin of the word all the way back to its roots in West Africa. Charlie Davenport might have been wrong about the origins of the name but it seems that he was right about those early associations: *boogie-woogie* is said to have developed as a musical entertainment in the saloon bars of Louisiana and Mississippi.

From about 1928, *boogie-woogie* began to grow in popularity, reaching a peak in the late 1930's and early 1940's when the famous exponents (including Meade Lux Lewis, Albert Ammons and Pete Johnson) made some of their classic recordings, now readily available in CD compilations. The vast majority of their compostions/improvisations fall into the form of the twelve-bar blues and feature a driving left-hand repeated figuration. This frequently consists of an arpeggio which includes the added sixth and/or the flattened seventh of the chord. Sometimes, however, a more powerful repetitive chordal figuration is heard, reminding us of the close association between *barrelhouse blues* and *boogie-woogie*.

Those who have tried to develop their own *boogie* piano-playing quickly discover the technical difficulties which are inherent in maintaining a mobile and rhythmic left-hand figuration whilst also giving thought to what the right-hand is playing. In *boogie* duets, the task is thankfully shared and if the *secondo* player, who of necessity is cast in the rôle of the accompanist, feels that he or she has drawn the shorter straw, then those rôles can always be reversed in the next performance.

Another very good reason for exchanging parts is to share the opportunity to improvise. The original *boogie-woogie* pianists were adept improvisers, of course, and *primo* players might very well want to depart from the printed page themselves from time to time, creating their own *riffs*, playing chords with *tremolo* ar making any other changes which will bring their performance closer to the spirit of the original *boogie-woogie* style.

MIKE CORNICK *January, 1999*

BOOGIE-WOOGIE

DIE GENAUEN ANFÄNGE JENES Klavier-Stils zu bestimmen, den wir heute als Boogie-Woogie bezeichnen, oder auch nur festzustellen, woher er eigentlich seinen Namen hat, ist sehr schwierig. Von allen möglichen Erklärungen gilt jene, dass der Begriff von Charlie „Cow Cow" Davenport (geboren 1895 in Alabama) erfunden wurde, heute als eher unwahrscheinlich. Er hat den Ausdruck mit dem Bogey-Man, dem „Schwarzen Mann" und den Assoziationen dieser Musik mit der einfachen Lebensart in Verbindung gebracht. Doch gibt es zumindest eine Quelle, welche die Entstehung des Begriffs bis zu seinen Ursprüngen im westlichen Afrika zurückverfolgt. Charlie Davenport mag sich vielleicht in Bezug auf die Herkunft des Namens geirrt haben, doch mit den frühen Assoziationen des Begriffs lag er richtig: Der Boogie-Woogie soll sich als musikalische Unterhaltung in den Salons von Lousiana und Mississippi entwickelt haben.

Von etwa 1928 an begann der Boogie-Woogie an Popularität zu gewinnen und erreichte seinen Höhepunkt in den späten 30er und frühen 40er Jahren, als berühmte Vertreter wie Meade Lux Lewis, Albert Ammons und Pete Johnson einige ihrer klassischen Aufnahmen machten, die heute noch als CD-Reihen erhältlich sind. Die meisten ihrer Kompositionen und Improvisationen haben die Form des 12-Takt-Blues mit ostinaten Bassfiguren. Diese haben zumeist die Form eines Arpeggios, wobei dem Akkord die übermäßige Sexte und/oder verminderte Septime hinzugefügt wird. Manchmal sind jedoch auch kräftigere Akkordfiguren zu hören, die an die enge Verwandtschaft des Boogie-Woogie mit dem Barrelhouse Blues erinnern.

Wer versucht, beim Boogie-Spiel seinen eigenen Stil zu entwickeln, entdeckt sehr schnell, wie schwierig es ist, die beweglichen und rhythmischen Figuren der linken Hand aufrecht zu erhalten und zugleich daran zu denken, was die rechte Hand zu spielen hat. Bei Boogie-Duetten wird diese Aufgabe geteilt, und wenn der *Secondo*, der zwangsläufig die Begleitung zu spielen hat, das Gefühl hat, er hätte den kürzeren gezogen, so kann beim nächsten Mal einfach ein Rollentausch vorgenommen werden.

Ein weiterer guter Grund für einen Wechsel der Parts ist die Möglichkeit zu improvisieren. Die frühen Boogie-Woogie-Spieler waren Meister der Improvisation, und Klavierspieler könnten sehr rasch den Wunsch verspüren, sich von Zeit zu Zeit von den gedruckten Noten zu lösen, Akkorde im *Tremolo* zu spielen oder die eine oder andere Veränderung vorzunehmen, die sie dem ursprünglichen Boogie-Woogie-Stil näherbringt.

MIKE CORNICK
Jänner 1999

Before you start…
an important note about rhythm!

All the pieces in this book are written using the rhythmic convention:

This simply means that all quaver movement (including tied quavers and rests) should be played with a 'swing' so that, for example:

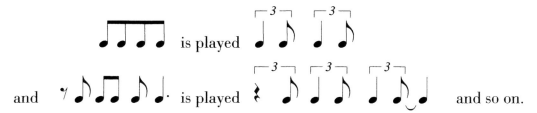

Tremolos

PRIMO players may wish to enhance their performance with the judicious use of tremolo on some of the right-hand chords which contain three notes. Such chords arise in *Intermezzo* and *Freight Train Boogie Blues*.

For example, the opening of *Intermezzo* could be played:

Und bevor Sie beginnen…
noch einige wichtige Bemerkungen zum Rhythmus!

Bei allen Stücken dieses Bandes wird folgender Rhythmus verwendet:

Das bedeutet, dass alle Achtelbewegungen – auch gebundene Achteln und Pausen – im „Swing" gespielt werden sollten.
Zum Beispiel:

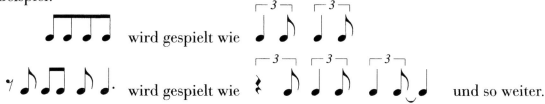

Tremolos

Der Stimmführende kann nach Wunsch bei einigen Akkorden der rechten Hand, die drei Noten enthalten, gezielt Tremolos einsetzen. Solche Akkorde finden sich in *Intermezzo* und *Freight Train Boogie Blues*.

Die Einleitung des *Intermezzo* könnte zum Beispiel so gespielt werden:

THE METAMORPHIC ROCK BOOGIE

Mike Cornick

Up-tempo swing ($\quarternote$ = 170)

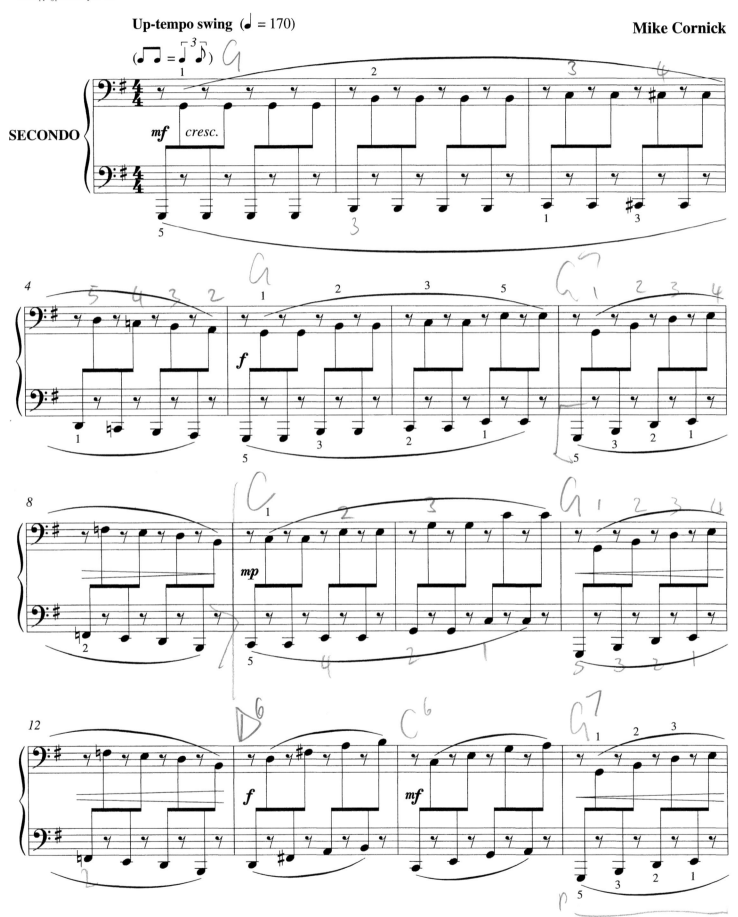

Universal Edition UE 18 796

THE METAMORPHIC ROCK BOOGIE

4

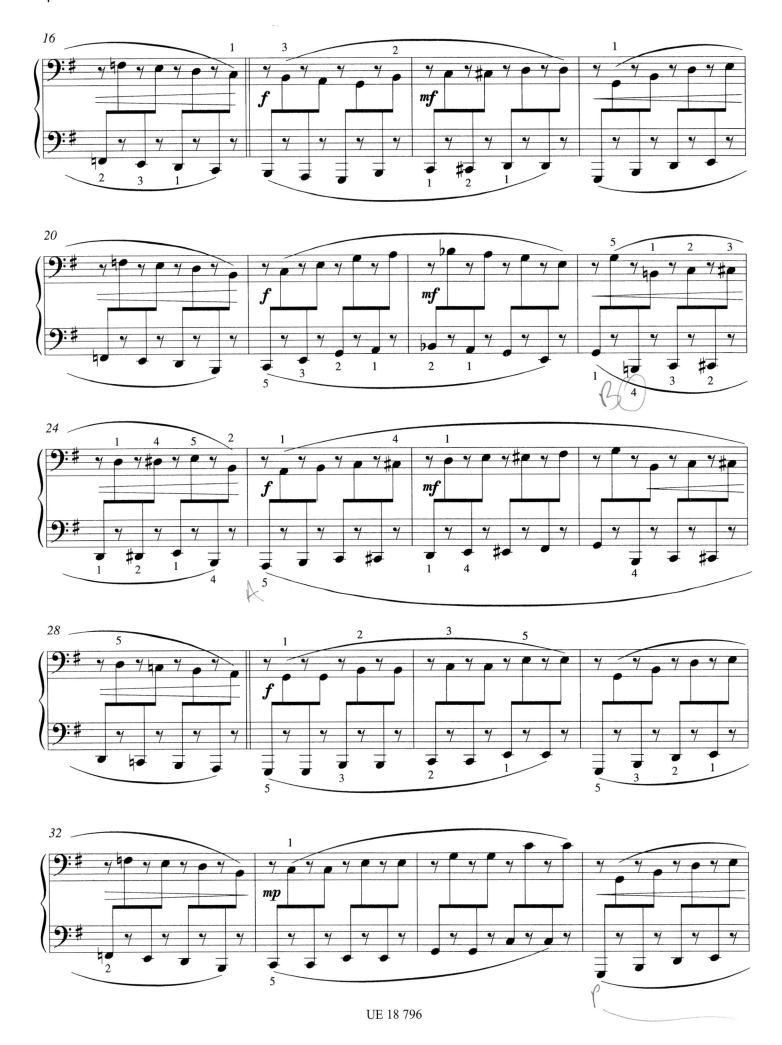

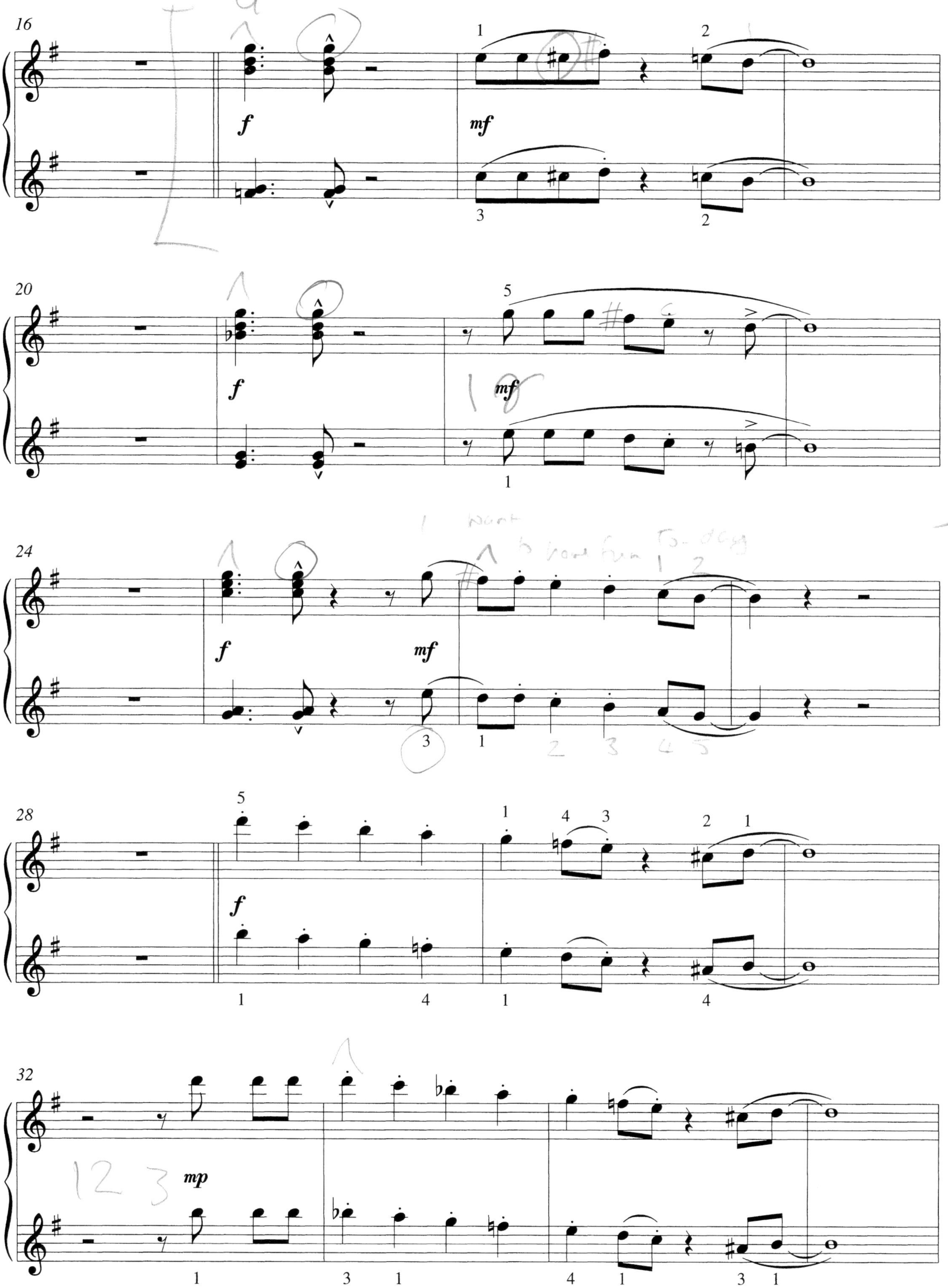
16
f
mf
20
f
mf
24
f
mf
28
f
32
mp

6

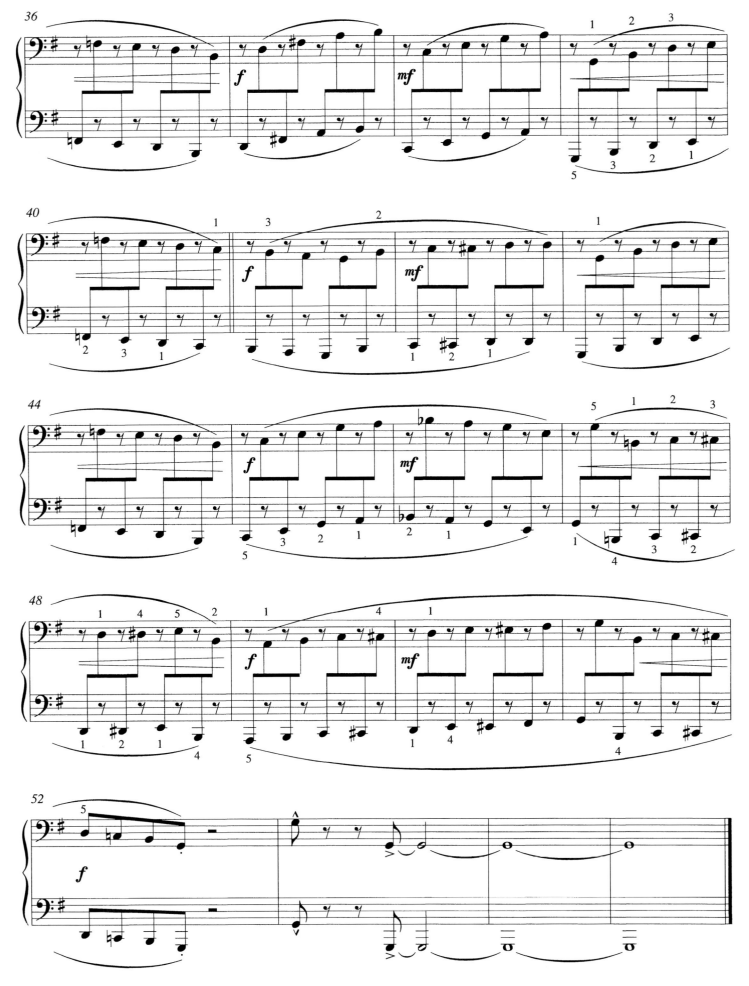

COUNTRY BOOGIE

Mike Cornick

Just ambling along (♩ = 105)

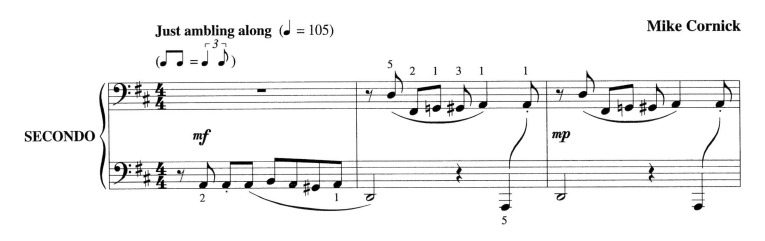

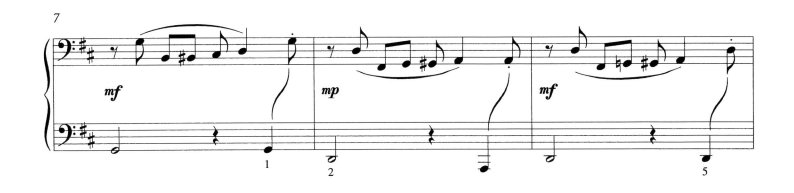

COUNTRY BOOGIE

Just ambling along ($\quad$ = 105)

Mike Cornick

PRIMO

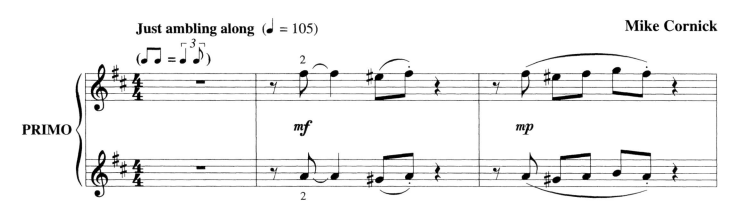

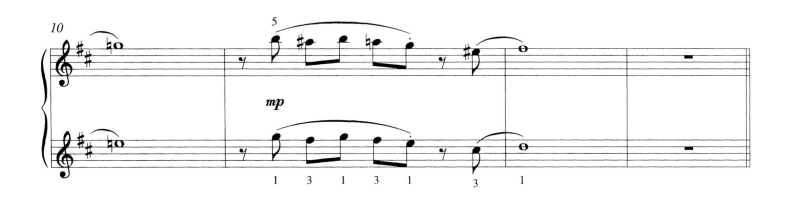

10

DISSONANT BOOGIE

Mike Cornick

Up-tempo boogie swing! (♩ = 170)

SECONDO

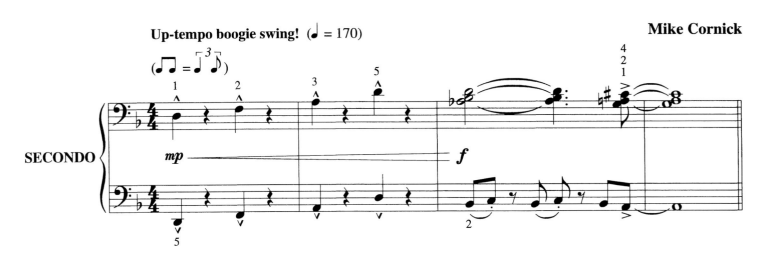

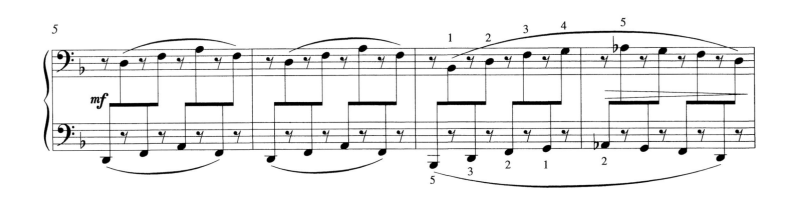

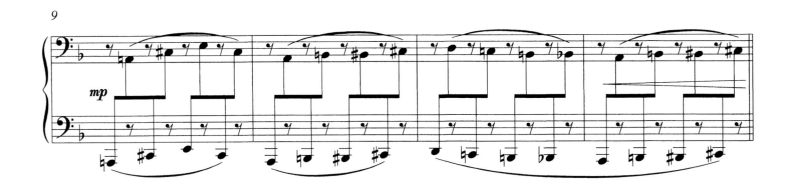

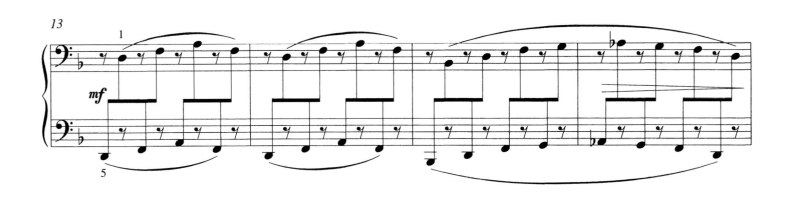

DISSONANT BOOGIE

Up-tempo boogie swing! (♩ = 170)

Mike Cornick

PRIMO

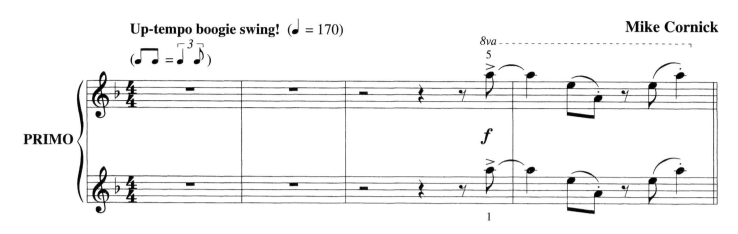

14

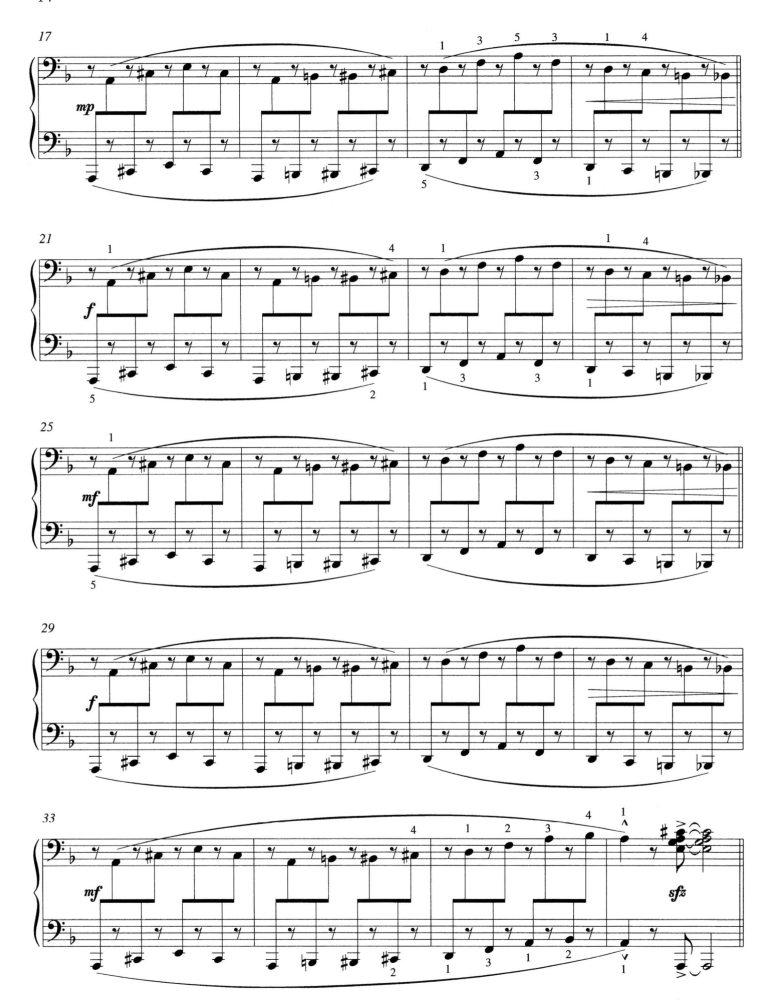

16

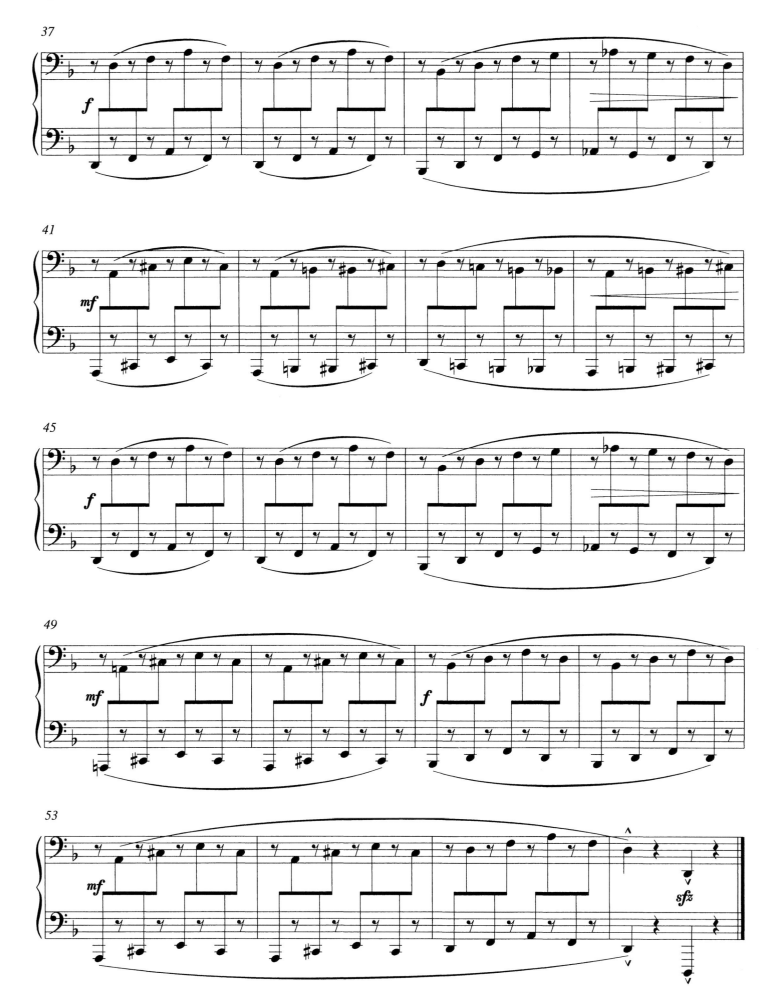

INTERMEZZO

Mike Cornick

INTERMEZZO

Mike Cornick

THOSE OLD FASHIONED BOOGIE BLUES

Mike Cornick

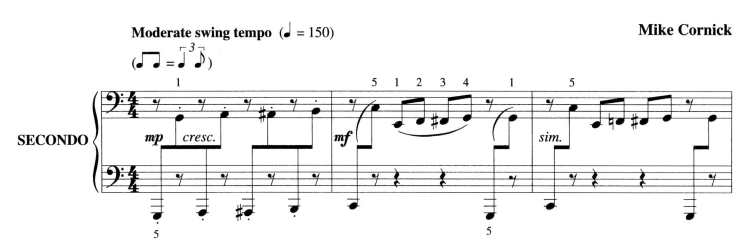

THOSE OLD FASHIONED BOOGIE BLUES

Mike Cornick

24

FREIGHT TRAIN BOOGIE BLUES

Mike Cornick

FREIGHT TRAIN BOOGIE BLUES

Mike Cornick

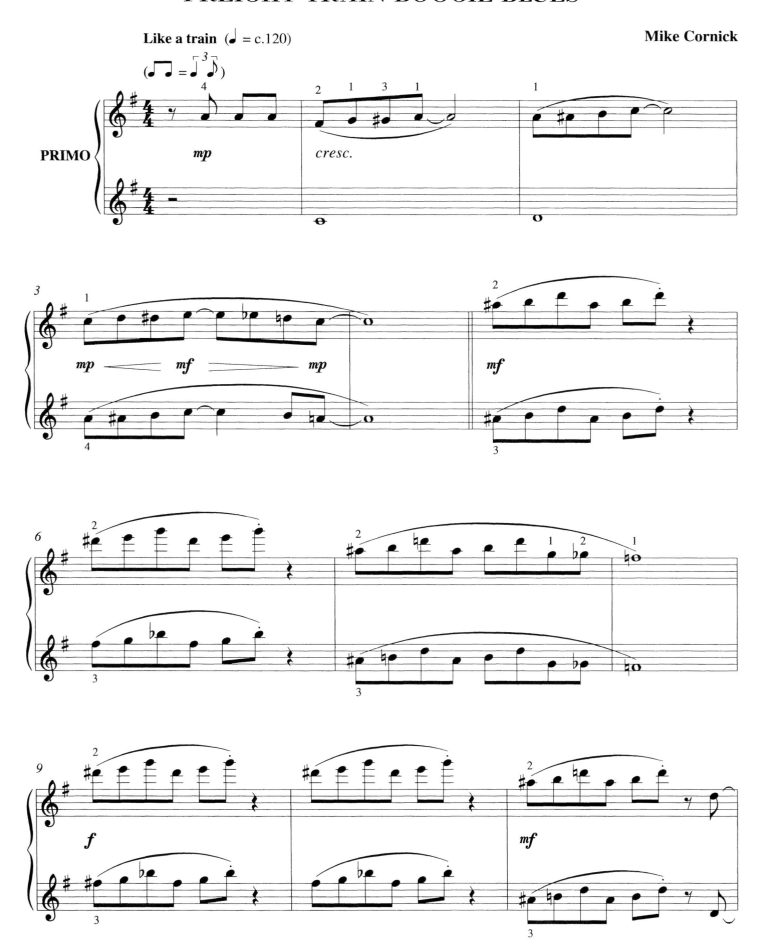

28

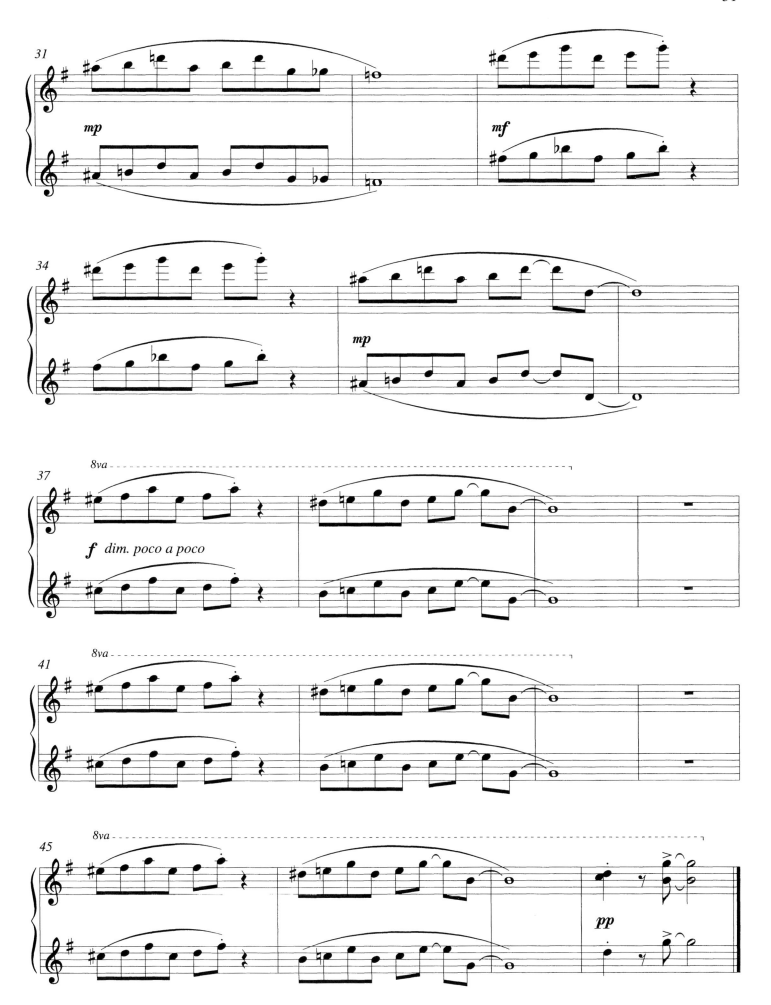

UE
Edition
Universal

MIKE CORNICK studied composition at Trinity College London and has subsequently taught music in Primary, Middle and Secondary schools and to Adult Education classes. He is best known for his jazz piano publications from which many selections have been made for graded piano examinations. Mike Cornick currently teaches piano and keyboard in a number of London Secondary schools.

Further titles by Mike Cornick

SOLO

Boogie Piano Book	(3–4)*	UE 16 592
Barrel House Piano	(5–6)	UE 17 375
Dixieland Piano	(4–6)	UE 21 025
Piano Ragtime	(4–5)	UE 30 413
Blue Piano	(4–6)	UE 19 762
Latin Piano	(3–6)	UE 17 365
Take Another 10 – Piano	(3-6)	UE 21 171
Easy Bar Piano – Rock & Pop (with CD)	(2–5)	UE 31 843 (Germ.)
Easy Bar Piano – Rock & Pop (with CD)	(2–5)	UE 31 843E (Eng.)
Easy Jazzy Piano 1	(2–5)	UE 16 550
Easy Jazzy Piano 2	(3–5)	UE 16 590
Jazz After Hours	(4–6)	UE 21 099
The Christmas Keyboard Songbook	(1–2)	UE 21 076
On The Right Track 1 (with CD)	(2–3)	UE 21 124
On The Right Track 2 (with CD)	(3–4)	UE 21 125
On The Right Track 3 (with CD)	(5–6)	UE 21 147
On The Right Track 4 (with CD)	(6–8)	UE 21 163

TUTORS

Jazz Improvisation for Piano & Keyboard (with CD)	(2–4)	UE 14 050
Start Pianojazz	(1–3)	UE 17 361
Pianojazz 1	(2–3)	UE 17 391
Pianojazz 2	(3–4)	UE 17 392
Pianojazz 3	(5-6)	UE 17 393
Skillbuilder 1	(2–3)	UE 21 077
Skillbuilder 2	(3–4)	UE 21 078
Skillbuilder 3	(5–6)	UE 21 079

4 HANDS (6 HANDS)

Blue Piano Duets	(6)	UE 21 006
Boogie Piano Duets	(4–5)	UE 18 796
Easy Jazzy Duets	(2–4)	UE 16 577
Jazzy Duets Piano 1	(3–4)	UE 19 756
Jazzy Duets Piano 2	(3–5)	UE 16 536
Latin Piano Duets	(4–6)	UE 21 007
Piano Ragtime Duets	(4–5)	UE 16 591
Three Pieces For 6 Hands at 1 Piano	(6–7)	UE 21 123

*Approximate Gradings 1–8 = Easy to Advanced

www.universaledition.com
vienna · london · new york